Key Stage 2

Multiplying and Dividing

Steve Mills and Hilary Koll

Name _____

Schofield & Sims

Introduction

Understanding how multiplication and division work is as important as knowing when and how to carry them out. In this learning workbook you will learn and practise different ways to multiply and divide numbers using both mental and written methods. This is because trying each method will help you to build a better understanding of what is happening as you multiply and divide.

How to use this book

Before you start using this book, write your name in the name box on the first page.

Then decide how to begin. If you want a complete course on multiplication and division, you should work right through the book from beginning to end. Another way to use the book is to dip into it when you want to find out about a particular topic. The contents page will help you to find the pages you need.

Whichever way you choose, don't try to do too much at once – it's better to work through the book in short bursts.

When you have found the topic you want to study, look out for these icons, which mark different parts of the text:

Activities

This icon shows you the activities that you should complete. You write your answers in the spaces provided. You might find it useful to have some scrap paper to work on for some of the activities. After you have worked through all the activities on the page, turn to pages A1 to A3 at the centre of the book to check your answers. When you are sure that you understand the topic, put a tick in the box beside it on the Contents page.

On pages 11 and 17, you will find **Progress Tests**. These contain questions that will check your understanding of the topics that you have worked through so far. Check your answers on page A4. It is important that you correct any mistakes before moving on to the next section.

At the back of the book you will find a **Final Test**. This will check your understanding of all the topics (page 26).

Explanation

This text explains the topic and gives examples. Make sure you read it before you start the activities.

Scrap Paper

This icon tells you when you may need to use scrap paper to work out your answers.

Fascinating Facts

This text gives you useful background information about the subject.

Contents

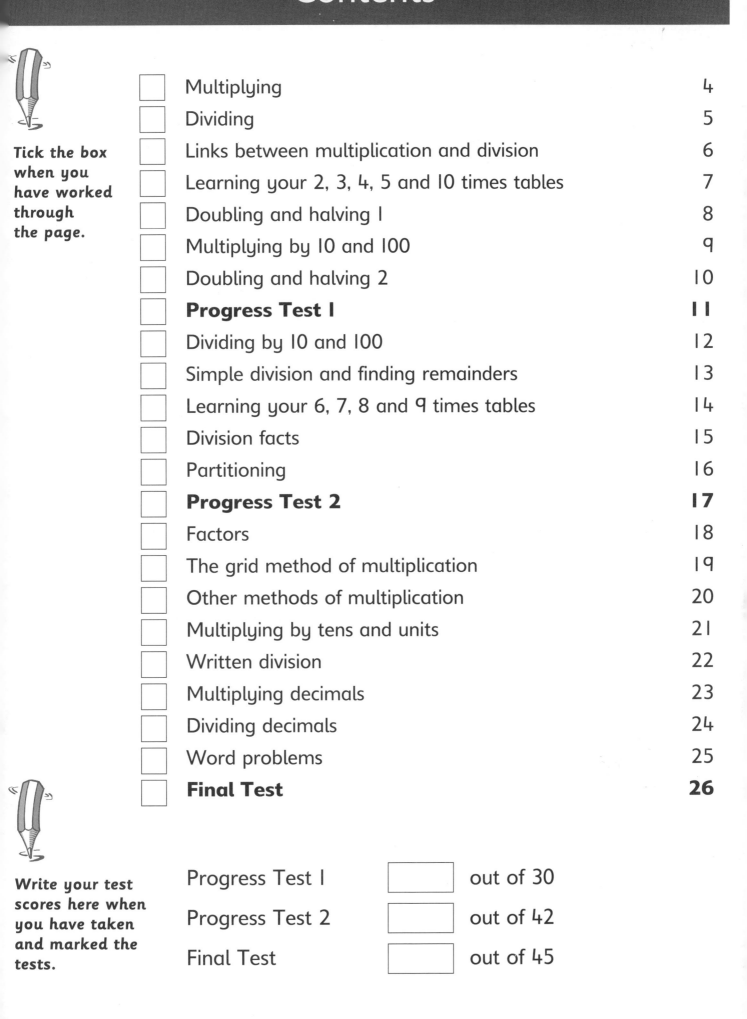

Tick the box when you have worked through the page.

Write your test scores here when you have taken and marked the tests.

Progress Test 1   [   ] out of 30

Progress Test 2   [   ] out of 42

Final Test   [   ] out of 45

Multiplying

Multiplication is just a quick way of adding lots of the same number. Instead of adding **6 + 6 + 6 + 6 + 6** we can say 'five lots of six' or 'five times six'.

We use a multiplication sign (×) when we multiply numbers together.

$$5 \times 6 = 30$$

Multiplication is the opposite of division and division is the opposite of multiplication.
If we multiply by a number and then divide by it we are left with the number we started with.

$$5 \times 6 \div 6 = 5$$

Multiplication words

These words often mean **multiply**:

times	groups of	product
multiplied by	lots of	double

It doesn't matter which way round you do a multiplication question, the answer will be the same.

$$\boxed{4} \times \boxed{8} = \boxed{32}$$

$$\boxed{8} \times \boxed{4} = \boxed{32}$$

1. Answer these questions.

a) 4 × 5 = _____   5 × 4 = _____

b) 3 × 7 = _____   7 × 3 = _____

c) 2 × 9 = _____   9 × 2 = _____

d) 5 × 3 = _____   3 × 5 = _____

e) 10 × 4 = _____   4 × 10 = _____

f) 6 × 10 = _____   10 × 6 = _____

Dividing

Division is what happens when we share things equally or divide things into equal groups.

$$8 \div 2 =$$

Equal sharing
8 children get into 2 teams.
There are 4 in each team.

Equal grouping
8 children get into teams of 2.
There are 4 teams.

$$8 \div 2 = 4 \qquad\qquad 8 \div 2 = 4$$

The answer is the same whichever method you use!

We use these signs to show division ÷ and $\overline{)}$

Division is the opposite of multiplication and multiplication is the opposite of division. If we divide by a number and then multiply by it we are left with the number we started with.

$$12 \div 6 \times 6 = 12$$

Division words

These words often mean **divide**:

| share | equal groups of | remainder |

| divided by | shared between | halve |

It **does** matter which way round you do a division question, the answer will **not** be the same.

$$\boxed{8} \div \boxed{4} = \boxed{2} \qquad\qquad \boxed{4} \div \boxed{8} = \boxed{\tfrac{1}{2}}$$

1. Answer these questions.

a) $8 \div 2 =$ ____ b) $10 \div 2 =$ ____ c) $12 \div 3 =$ ____ d) $15 \div 5 =$ ____

e) $16 \div 4 =$ ____ f) $9 \div 3 =$ ____ g) $10 \div 5 =$ ____ h) $20 \div 2 =$ ____

Links between multiplication and division

Links between multiplication and division

Multiplying and dividing are closely related. They are opposites, because one 'undoes' the other. The mathematical term for this is 'inverse'. We say that multiplication and division are **inverses**.

$6 \times 3 = 18$
$18 \div 3 = 6$

1. Follow the trains to find the answers, like this:

$$2 \times 4 \div 2 \times 3 \div 4 \times 2 \div 3 = \underline{\hspace{1cm}}$$

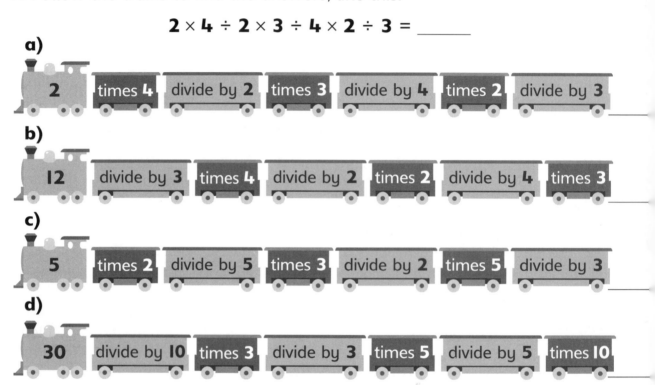

a)
2 | times **4** | divide by **2** | times **3** | divide by **4** | times **2** | divide by **3**

b)
12 | divide by **3** | times **4** | divide by **2** | times **2** | divide by **4** | times **3**

c)
5 | times **2** | divide by **5** | times **3** | divide by **2** | times **5** | divide by **3**

d)
30 | divide by **10** | times **3** | divide by **3** | times **5** | divide by **5** | times **10**

2. What do you notice about each of your answers? Why do you think this is?

_____

_____

_____

3. Use these multiplication and division facts to help you to answer the questions below.

$5 \times 4 = 20$	$20 \div 10 = 2$	$4 \times 3 = 12$
$15 \div 3 = 5$	$10 \times 4 = 40$	$25 \div 5 = 5$

a) $20 \div 5 = \underline{\hspace{1cm}}$

b) $40 \div 4 = \underline{\hspace{1cm}}$

c) $10 \times 2 = \underline{\hspace{1cm}}$

d) $5 \times 5 = \underline{\hspace{1cm}}$

e) $12 \div 3 = \underline{\hspace{1cm}}$

f) $5 \times 3 = \underline{\hspace{1cm}}$

Learning your 2, 3, 4, 5 and 10 times tables

You need to learn the facts below because they make multiplication questions easier.

2 ×	3 ×	4 ×	5 ×	10 ×
2 × 0 = 0	3 × 0 = 0	4 × 0 = 0	5 × 0 = 0	10 × 0 = 0
2 × 1 = 2	3 × 1 = 3	4 × 1 = 4	5 × 1 = 5	10 × 1 = 10
2 × 2 = 4	3 × 2 = 6	4 × 2 = 8	5 × 2 = 10	10 × 2 = 20
2 × 3 = 6	3 × 3 = 9	4 × 3 = 12	5 × 3 = 15	10 × 3 = 30
2 × 4 = 8	3 × 4 = 12	4 × 4 = 16	5 × 4 = 20	10 × 4 = 40
2 × 5 = 10	3 × 5 = 15	4 × 5 = 20	5 × 5 = 25	10 × 5 = 50
2 × 6 = 12	3 × 6 = 18	4 × 6 = 24	5 × 6 = 30	10 × 6 = 60
2 × 7 = 14	3 × 7 = 21	4 × 7 = 28	5 × 7 = 35	10 × 7 = 70
2 × 8 = 16	3 × 8 = 24	4 × 8 = 32	5 × 8 = 40	10 × 8 = 80
2 × 9 = 18	3 × 9 = 27	4 × 9 = 36	5 × 9 = 45	10 × 9 = 90
2 × 10 = 20	3 × 10 = 30	4 × 10 = 40	5 × 10 = 50	10 × 10 = 100

Did you know...

When you learn a tables fact you get two for the price of one! If you know one fact you automatically know another. So, with each fact you learn, turn it around to get another, e.g.

4 × 9 = 36 and **9 × 4 = 36**

When you are sure you know a fact in the tables above, tick it. Make sure you know its partner, and tick it too!

1. Cover the tables above and test yourself on these questions.

a) 4 × 5 = ____   b) 5 × 8 = ____   c) 3 × 7 = ____   d) 5 × 3 = ____

e) 10 × 9 = ____   f) 4 × 7 = ____   g) 5 × 5 = ____   h) 4 × 3 = ____

i) 2 × 5 = ____   j) 3 × 5 = ____   k) 4 × 2 = ____   l) 4 × 9 = ____

m) 10 × 4 = ____   n) 2 × 9 = ____   o) 3 × 10 = ____   p) 5 × 9 = ____

q) 3 × 6 = ____   r) 4 × 6 = ____   s) 2 × 6 = ____   t) 4 × 4 = ____

u) 2 × 3 = ____   v) 3 × 8 = ____   w) 5 × 7 = ____   x) 2 × 8 = ____

y) 3 × 9 = ____   z) 4 × 8 = ____

Doubling and halving 1

Times by 2		Multiply by 2		Twice

Doubling

To double a **2**-digit number we can use partitioning, like this:

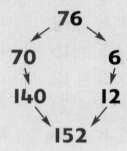

Partition the number into tens and units.

Multiply each number by **2**

Add the two numbers together.

1. Double these numbers.

    a) 19 _____   **b)** 23 _____   **c)** 36 _____   **d)** 42 _____   **e)** 45 _____

    f) 48 _____   **g)** 53 _____   **h)** 68 _____   **i)** 77 _____   **j)** 89 _____

Divide by 2		Half

Halving

To halve a **2**- or **3**-digit number we can use partitioning, like this:

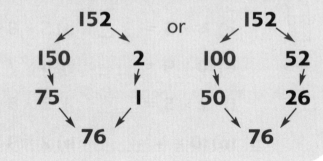

Partition the number.

Divide each number by **2**

Add the two numbers together.

2. Halve these numbers.

    a) 62 _____   **b)** 78 _____   **c)** 84 _____   **d)** 92 _____   **e)** 98 _____

    f) 104 _____   **g)** 126 _____   **h)** 132 _____   **i)** 168 _____   **j)** 178 _____

Multiplying by 10 and 100

Multiplying by 10
When multiplying by **10** move each digit of the other number **one** place to the **left**. We use zeros to show the empty columns.

637 × 10 = 6370

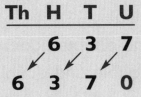

Multiplying by 100
When multiplying by **100** move each digit **two** places to the **left**. We use zeros to show the empty columns.

637 × 100 = 63 700

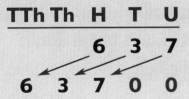

1. Multiply these numbers by 10

a) 9 → __90__   b) 25 → _____   c) 43 → _____

d) 80 → _____   e) 378 → _____   f) 593 → _____

g) 682 → _____   h) 8036 → _____   i) 6820 → _____

2. Change these prices from pounds to pence by multiplying by 100

a) £2 → __200p__   b) £9 → _____   c) £17 → _____

d) £69 → _____   e) £127 → _____   f) £659 → _____

g) £806 → _____   h) £2743 → _____   i) £5280 → _____

3. Change these lengths from metres to centimetres by multiplying by 100

a) 5m → __500cm__   b) 8m → _____   c) 23m → _____

d) 75m → _____   e) 341m → _____   f) 555m → _____

g) 904m → _____   h) 3680m → _____   i) 6900m → _____

Doubling and halving

Doubling can help you to multiply numbers.

To multiply a number:

by 2 – just double it $19 \times 2 = 38$

by 4 – double and double again $19 \times 2 = 38, 38 \times 2 = 76$

by 8 – double, double and double again $19 \times 2 = 38, 38 \times 2 = 76,$
$76 \times 2 = 152$

Halving can help you to divide numbers.

To divide a number:

by 2 – just halve it $128 \div 2 = 64$

by 4 – halve and halve again $128 \div 2 = 64, 64 \div 2 = 32$

by 8 – halve, halve and halve again $128 \div 2 = 64, 64 \div 2 = 32,$
$32 \div 2 = 16$

1. Answer these questions, using doubling and halving.

a) $7 \times 4 =$ _____   b) $7 \times 8 =$ _____   c) $9 \times 4 =$ _____   d) $25 \times 8 =$ ___

e) $48 \div 4 =$ _____   f) $48 \div 8 =$ _____   g) $52 \div 4 =$ ___   h) $64 \div 8 =$ __

If we want to multiply an even number by **5**,
we can halve the even number and double the **5**
This makes it easier because we can then
multiply by **10**

$5 \times 36 = 180$

(double)   (half)

$10 \times 18 = 180$

2. To answer these questions, **double** the first number and **halve** the other.

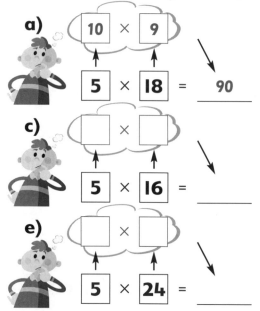

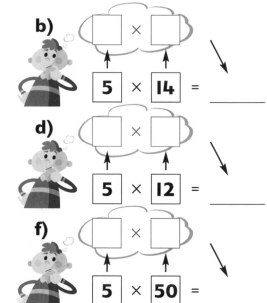

Progress Test 1

1. Follow the train to find the final answer.

 4 | times **3** | divide by **2** | times **4** | divide by **4** | times **2** | divide by **3** _____

2. Use these facts to help you to answer the questions below.

| $24 \div 3 = 8$ | $7 \times 5 = 35$ | $32 \div 4 = 8$ |

a) $4 \times 8 =$ _____ b) $3 \times 8 =$ _____ c) $35 \div 5 =$ _____

3. Answer these questions.

a) $4 \times 7 =$ _____ b) $5 \times 9 =$ _____ c) $3 \times 4 =$ _____

d) $10 \times 9 =$ _____ e) $4 \times 6 =$ _____ f) $5 \times 5 =$ _____

4. Use doubling and halving to answer these questions.

a) $13 \times 4 =$ _____ b) $8 \times 8 =$ _____ c) $13 \times 8 =$ _____

d) $72 \div 4 =$ _____ e) $108 \div 4 =$ _____ f) $56 \div 8 =$ _____

5. Multiply these numbers by 10

a) **28** → _____ b) **537** → _____ c) **2043** → _____

d) **308** → _____ e) **462** → _____ f) **1204** → _____

6. Multiply these numbers by 100

a) **16** → _____ b) **386** → _____ c) **4037** → _____

d) **80** → _____ e) **406** → _____ f) **3200** → _____

7. To answer these questions, **double** the first number and **halve** the other.

a)
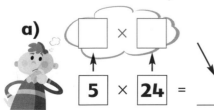
$5 \times 24 =$ _____

b)
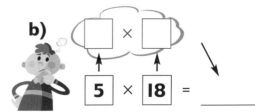
$5 \times 18 =$ _____

Dividing by 10 and 100

Dividing by 10
When dividing by **10** move each digit of the other number **one** place to the **right**.

57 300 ÷ 10 = 5730

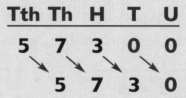

Dividing by 100
When dividing by **100** move each digit **two** places to the **right**.

57 300 ÷ 100 = 573

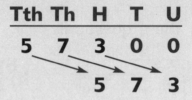

1. Divide these numbers by 10

a) 50 → _____   b) 70 → _____   c) 90 → _____

d) 100 → _____   e) 280 → _____   f) 670 → _____

g) 940 → _____   h) 4830 → _____   i) 5000 → _____

2. Change these prices from pence to pounds by dividing by 100

a) 300p → __£3__   b) 500p → _____   c) 800p → _____

d) 900p → _____   e) 1400p → _____   f) 2400p → _____

g) 36 200p → _____   h) 56 700p → _____   i) 40 000p → _____

3. Change these lengths from centimetres to metres by dividing by 100

a) 600cm → __6m__   b) 900cm → _____   c) 3400cm → _____

d) 5300cm → _____   e) 36 700cm → _____   f) 68 300cm → _____

g) 90 200cm → _____   h) 56 200cm → _____   i) 73 000cm → _____

Simple division and finding remainders

Finding remainders

If we share **12** biscuits between **3** people they each get **4**. There are no biscuits left over because **4** divides exactly into **12**.

$$12 \div 3 = 4$$

If we share **14** biscuits between **3** people they each get **4** but there are **2** biscuits left over.

$$14 \div 3 = 4 \text{ with } 2 \text{ left over}$$

We say **14** divided by **3** is **4** remainder **2**.

$$14 \div 3 = 4 \text{ r}2$$

1. Answer these questions.

a) $13 \div 3 =$ ___4 r1___   b) $11 \div 3 =$ _____   c) $14 \div 3 =$ _____

d) $17 \div 3 =$ _____   e) $19 \div 3 =$ _____   f) $25 \div 3 =$ _____

We can show multiples of a number on a counting stick. Count up in **4**s from zero to show the multiples of **4**. They are shown beneath this line.

| 0 | 1 | 2 | 3 | 4 | 5 | 6 | 7 | 8 | 9 | 10 |

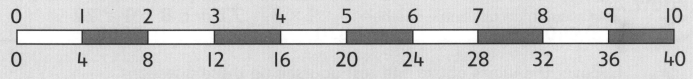

| 0 | 4 | 8 | 12 | 16 | 20 | 24 | 28 | 32 | 36 | 40 |

Can you see how to find the answer to these? $20 \div 4 = 5$ $24 \div 4 = 6$

If the number to be divided is not a multiple of **4** we can give our answer with a remainder, like this... $25 \div 4 = 6 \text{ r}1$

Look for the multiple of **4** just less than the number: **24** is **1** less than **25** so there is a remainder of **1**.

2. Answer these questions.

a) $19 \div 4 =$ _____   b) $22 \div 4 =$ _____   c) $27 \div 4 =$ _____

d) $29 \div 4 =$ _____   e) $33 \div 4 =$ _____   f) $35 \div 4 =$ _____

3. Use the multiples of 5 to answer these.

a) $19 \div 5 =$ _____   b) $24 \div 5 =$ _____   c) $29 \div 5 =$ _____

d) $37 \div 5 =$ _____   e) $43 \div 5 =$ _____   f) $46 \div 5 =$ _____

Learning your 6, 7, 8 and 9 times tables

You need to learn the facts below because they make multiplication questions easier.

6 ×	7 ×	8 ×	9 ×
6 × 0 = 0	7 × 0 = 0	8 × 0 = 0	9 × 0 = 0
6 × 1 = 6	7 × 1 = 7	8 × 1 = 8	9 × 1 = 9
6 × 2 = 12	7 × 2 = 14	8 × 2 = 16	9 × 2 = 18
6 × 3 = 18	7 × 3 = 21	8 × 3 = 24	9 × 3 = 27
6 × 4 = 24	7 × 4 = 28	8 × 4 = 32	9 × 4 = 36
6 × 5 = 30	7 × 5 = 35	8 × 5 = 40	9 × 5 = 45
6 × 6 = 36	7 × 6 = 42	8 × 6 = 48	9 × 6 = 54
6 × 7 = 42	7 × 7 = 49	8 × 7 = 56	9 × 7 = 63
6 × 8 = 48	7 × 8 = 56	8 × 8 = 64	9 × 8 = 72
6 × 9 = 54	7 × 9 = 63	8 × 9 = 72	9 × 9 = 81
6 × 10 = 60	7 × 10 = 70	8 × 10 = 80	9 × 10 = 90

Did you know... Some of these facts can be tricky, but remember, if you know one fact you automatically know another   **9 × 8 = 72** and **8 × 9 = 72**

1. Cover the tables above and test yourself on these questions.

a) 6 × 5 = _____   b) 7 × 8 = _____   c) 7 × 7 = _____   d) 6 × 3 = _____

e) 10 × 9 = _____   f) 8 × 6 = _____   g) 8 × 8 = _____   h) 9 × 7 = _____

i) 8 × 5 = _____   j) 7 × 5 = _____   k) 7 × 4 = _____   l) 8 × 7 = _____

m) 9 × 9 = _____   n) 6 × 7 = _____   o) 9 × 6 = _____   p) 6 × 6 = _____

q) 8 × 3 = _____   r) 6 × 8 = _____   s) 8 × 9 = _____   t) 9 × 5 = _____

u) 6 × 9 = _____   v) 9 × 8 = _____   w) 7 × 10 = _____   x) 7 × 9 = _____

2. Practise your tables with a set of playing cards. Take out the picture cards and put the rest face down in a pile. Turn two over together and multiply. Keep the cards if you know the answer. Check any you're not sure of. How quickly can you finish the pile?

Answers to Activities

Page 4

1. a) 20, 20   b) 21, 21
   c) 18, 18   d) 15, 15
   e) 40, 40   f) 60, 60

Page 5

1. a) 4   b) 5   c) 4   d) 3
   e) 4   f) 3   g) 2   h) 10

Page 6

1. a) 2
   b) 12
   c) 5
   d) 30

2. The answer is the same as the number you started with. For each multiplication there is a similar division that undoes it.

3. a) 4   b) 10   c) 20
   d) 25   e) 4   f) 15

Page 7

1. a) 20   b) 40   c) 21   d) 15
   e) 90   f) 28   g) 25   h) 12
   i) 10   j) 15   k) 8   l) 36
   m) 40   n) 18   o) 30   p) 45
   q) 18   r) 24   s) 12   t) 16
   u) 6   v) 24   w) 35   x) 16
   y) 27   z) 32

Page 8

1. a) 38   b) 46   c) 72   d) 84   e) 90
   f) 96   g) 106   h) 136   i) 154   j) 178

2. a) 31   b) 39   c) 42   d) 46   e) 49
   f) 52   g) 63   h) 66   i) 84   j) 89

Page 9

1. a) 90   b) 250   c) 430
   d) 800   e) 3780   f) 5930
   g) 6820   h) 80 360   i) 68 200

2. a) 200p   b) 900p   c) 1700p
   d) 6900p   e) 12 700p   f) 65 900p
   g) 80 600p   h) 274 300p   i) 528 000p

3. a) 500cm   b) 800cm   c) 2300cm
   d) 7500cm   e) 34 100cm
   f) 55 500cm   g) 90 400cm
   h) 368 000cm   i) 690 000cm

Page 10

1. a) 28   b) 56   c) 36   d) 200
   e) 12   f) 6   g) 13   h) 8

2. a) 90   b) 70
   c) 80   d) 60
   e) 120   f) 250

Answers to Activities

Page 12

1. a) 5   b) 7   c) 9
   d) 10   e) 28   f) 67
   g) 94   h) 483   i) 500
2. a) £3   b) £5   c) £8
   d) £9   e) £14   f) £24
   g) £362   h) £567   i) £400
3. a) 6m   b) 9m   c) 34m
   d) 53m   e) 367m   f) 683m
   g) 902m   h) 562m   i) 730m

Page 13

1. a) 4r1   b) 3r2   c) 4r2
   d) 5r2   e) 6r1   f) 8r1
2. a) 4r3   b) 5r2   c) 6r3
   d) 7r1   e) 8r1   f) 8r3
3. a) 3r4   b) 4r4   c) 5r4
   d) 7r2   e) 8r3   f) 9r1

Page 14

1. a) 30   b) 56   c) 49   d) 18
   e) 90   f) 48   g) 64   h) 63
   i) 40   j) 35   k) 28   l) 56
   m) 81   n) 42   o) 54   p) 36
   q) 24   r) 48   s) 72   t) 45
   u) 54   v) 72   w) 70   x) 63

Page 15

1. a) 7   b) 5   c) 5   d) 3
   e) 4   f) 6   g) 6   h) 8
   i) 4   j) 6   k) 5   l) 7
   m) 6   n) 8   o) 9   p) 7
   q) 8   r) 9   s) 8   t) 9
   u) 7   v) 9   w) 7   x) 10

Page 16

1. a) 125   b) 136   c) 195
   d) 252   e) 301   f) 260
   g) 384   h) 497   i) 656
2. a) 496   b) 820   c) 1245
   d) 2052   e) 2838   f) 3108
   g) 3948   h) 5128   i) 7038

Page 18

1. a) 12 → 1, 2, 3, 4, 6, 12
   b) 16 → 1, 2, 4, 8, 16
   c) 24 → 1, 2, 3, 4, 6, 8, 12, 24
   d) 30 → 1, 2, 3, 5, 6, 10, 15, 30
   e) 36 → 1, 2, 3, 4, 6, 9, 12, 18, 36
   f) 42 → 1, 2, 3, 6, 7, 14, 21, 42
2. a) 200   b) 90   c) 300
   d) 420   e) 480   f) 480
   g) 600   h) 420   i) 720

Page 19

1. a) 992   b) 1935
   c) 2832   d) 3773
   e) 5056   f) 6714
   g) 10 536   h) 18 140
   i) 34 374   j) 43 995

Page 20

1. a) 2315   b) 2288   c) 2916
   d) 11 780   e) 43 533   f) 59 776
2. a) 1428   b) 3090   c) 4356
   d) 12 344   e) 38 003   f) 50 992

Answers to Activities

1. a) 5797   b) 14 496   c) 23 220
   d) 20 634   e) 17 974   f) 32 562
2. a) 7848   b) 19 866   c) 30 128
   d) 37 062   e) 385 296   f) 847 295

1. a) 27   b) 23   c) 21
   d) 63   e) 47   f) 57
2. a) 37   b) 31   c) 24
   d) 73   e) 82   f) 87

1. a) 39·2   b) 39   c) 49·8
   d) 25·8   e) 42·28   f) 19·12
2. a) 15·6   b) 15·552   c) 35·796
   d) 38·661   e) 55·366   f) 70·512

1. a) 2·9   b) 2·6   c) 3·1
   d) 1·46   e) 1·97   f) 1·08
   g) 9·3   h) 0·86   i) 0·84
   j) 6·98   k) 1·36   l) 23·5

1·36	2·4	3·87	1·9	4·82	3·6
23·5	4·04	9·27	3·1	1·46	9·3
2·9	0·84	2·6	6·98	8·1	0·86
8·3	7·56	4·9	3·7	8·64	1·97
2·7	0·46	6·2	4·86	3·9	1·08

1. £12.36
2. a) £24 672
   b) £22 802
3. 32

Answers to Tests

PROGRESS TEST 1 Page 11

1. 4
2. a) 32   b) 24   c) 7
3. a) 28   b) 45   c) 12
   d) 90   e) 24   f) 25
4. a) 52   b) 64   c) 104
   d) 18   e) 27   f) 7
5. a) 280   b) 5370   c) 20 430
   d) 3080   e) 4620   f) 12 040
6. a) 1600   b) 38 600   c) 403 700
   d) 8000   e) 40 600   f) 320 000
7. a) 120   b) 90

Total marks = 30

PROGRESS TEST 2 Page 17

1. a) 7   b) 9   c) 30
   d) 64   e) 238   f) 510
2. a) 6   b) 8   c) 13
   d) 70   e) 318   f) 890
3. a) 4r3   b) 7r1   c) 5r2
   d) 7r1   e) 6r3   f) 8r3
4. a) 81   b) 42   c) 54
   d) 24   e) 48   f) 72
5. a) 6   b) 5   c) 7
   d) 8   e) 9   f) 7
6. a) 120   b) 160   c) 240
   d) 1200   e) 2000   f) 3600
7. a) 108   b) 270   c) 294
   d) 1482   e) 2961   f) 5856

Total marks = 42

FINAL TEST Pages 26 to 28

1. a) 9   b) 54   c) 42
2. a) 56   b) 63   c) 40   d) 49
   e) 48   f) 45   g) 28   h) 27
3. a) 360   b) 450
   c) 350   d) 2300
4. a) 290   b) 6080   c) 91 270
5. a) 2400   b) 53 600   c) 826 700
6. a) 73   b) 169   c) 300
7. a) 62   b) 73   c) 860
8. a) 9r3   b) 9r5   c) 7r1
9. a) 1, 2, 4, 8, 16, 32
   b) 1, 2, 3, 4, 6, 8, 9, 12, 18, 24, 36, 72
10. a) 300   b) 630
11. a) 2860   b) 61 434
12. a) 42 282   b) 285 300
13. a) 94   b) 96
14. a) 31·6   b) 22·724
15. a) 5·8   b) 0·76
16. 280

Total marks = 45

Division facts

The division facts below are linked to your **6**, **7**, **8**, **9** and **10** times tables. Try to learn them because they make division questions easier.

÷ 6	÷ 7	÷ 8	÷ 9	÷ 10
6 ÷ 6 = 1	7 ÷ 7 = 1	8 ÷ 8 = 1	9 ÷ 9 = 1	10 ÷ 10 = 1
12 ÷ 6 = 2	14 ÷ 7 = 2	16 ÷ 8 = 2	18 ÷ 9 = 2	20 ÷ 10 = 2
18 ÷ 6 = 3	21 ÷ 7 = 3	24 ÷ 8 = 3	27 ÷ 9 = 3	30 ÷ 10 = 3
24 ÷ 6 = 4	28 ÷ 7 = 4	32 ÷ 8 = 4	36 ÷ 9 = 4	40 ÷ 10 = 4
30 ÷ 6 = 5	35 ÷ 7 = 5	40 ÷ 8 = 5	45 ÷ 9 = 5	50 ÷ 10 = 5
36 ÷ 6 = 6	42 ÷ 7 = 6	48 ÷ 8 = 6	54 ÷ 9 = 6	60 ÷ 10 = 6
42 ÷ 6 = 7	49 ÷ 7 = 7	56 ÷ 8 = 7	63 ÷ 9 = 7	70 ÷ 10 = 7
48 ÷ 6 = 8	56 ÷ 7 = 8	64 ÷ 8 = 8	72 ÷ 9 = 8	80 ÷ 10 = 8
54 ÷ 6 = 9	63 ÷ 7 = 9	72 ÷ 8 = 9	81 ÷ 9 = 9	90 ÷ 10 = 9
60 ÷ 6 = 10	70 ÷ 7 = 10	80 ÷ 8 = 10	90 ÷ 9 = 10	100 ÷ 10 = 10

Did you know...

Some of these facts can be tricky but remember they are the opposite of multiplication facts. So if you need to know **63 ÷ 9** you can think about how many **9**s in **63**.

63 ÷ 9 = 7 and **7 × 9 = 63**

1. Cover the tables above and test yourself on these questions.

a) 42 ÷ 6 = ___   b) 35 ÷ 7 = ___   c) 40 ÷ 8 = ___   d) 27 ÷ 9 = ___

e) 36 ÷ 9 = ___   f) 48 ÷ 8 = ___   g) 42 ÷ 7 = ___   h) 64 ÷ 8 = ___

i) 32 ÷ 8 = ___   j) 36 ÷ 6 = ___   k) 45 ÷ 9 = ___   l) 49 ÷ 7 = ___

m) 54 ÷ 9 = ___   n) 56 ÷ 7 = ___   o) 72 ÷ 8 = ___   p) 63 ÷ 9 = ___

q) 72 ÷ 9 = ___   r) 63 ÷ 7 = ___   s) 48 ÷ 6 = ___   t) 81 ÷ 9 = ___

u) 56 ÷ 8 = ___   v) 54 ÷ 6 = ___   w) 70 ÷ 10 = ___   x) 100 ÷ 10 = ___

Partitioning

For work on this page you need to know how to multiply numbers like **20**, **30**, **40**, **50**... or **200**, **300**, **400**... by a single number. It's easy...

$\boxed{50 \times 6} = 5 \times 6 \times 10$
$= 30 \times 10 = 300$

$\boxed{700 \times 5} = 7 \times 5 \times 100$
$= 35 \times 100 = 3500$

Partitioning into tens and units

Partitioning means splitting numbers up, such as into tens and units. We do this to make calculations easier:

- write the question $\qquad$ $46 \times 7 =$ (Approximately $50 \times 7 = 350$)

- split **46** into **40** and **6** $\qquad$ $40 \times 7 + 6 \times 7$

- multiply each of these by **7** $\qquad$ $280 \quad + \quad 42 = 322$

1. Use partitioning to multiply these numbers.

a) $25 \times 5 = $ _____

b) $34 \times 4 = $ _____

c) $39 \times 5 = $ _____

d) $42 \times 6 = $ _____

e) $43 \times 7 = $ _____

f) $52 \times 5 = $ _____

g) $64 \times 6 = $ _____

h) $71 \times 7 = $ _____

i) $82 \times 8 = $ _____

Partitioning into hundreds, tens and units

We can also partition numbers into hundreds, tens and units to help us to multiply.

- write the question $\qquad$ $237 \times 6 =$ (Approximately $250 \times 6 = 1500$)

- split **237** into **200**, **30** and **7** $\qquad$ $200 \times 6 + 30 \times 6 + 7 \times 6$

- multiply each of these by **6** $\qquad$ $1200 \quad + \quad 180 + 42 = 1422$

2. Use partitioning to multiply these numbers.

a) $124 \times 4 = $ _____

b) $164 \times 5 = $ _____

c) $249 \times 5 = $ _____

d) $342 \times 6 = $ _____

e) $473 \times 6 = $ _____

f) $518 \times 6 = $ _____

g) $564 \times 7 = $ _____

h) $641 \times 8 = $ _____

i) $782 \times 9 = $ _____

Progress Test 2

1. Divide these numbers by 10

    a) 70 → _____   **b) 90** → _____   **c) 300** → _____

    d) 640 → _____   **e) 2380** → _____   **f) 5100** → _____

2. Divide these numbers by 100

    a) 600 → _____   **b) 800** → _____   **c) 1300** → _____

    d) 7000 → _____ **e) 31800** → _____ **f) 89000** → _____

3. Answer these questions, giving remainders in your answers.

    a) $19 \div 4 =$ _____   **b)** $22 \div 3 =$ _____   **c)** $27 \div 5 =$ _____

    d) $29 \div 4 =$ _____   **e)** $33 \div 5 =$ _____   **f)** $35 \div 4 =$ _____

4. Answer these questions.

    a) $9 \times 9 =$ _____   **b)** $6 \times 7 =$ _____   **c)** $9 \times 6 =$ _____

    d) $8 \times 3 =$ _____   **e)** $6 \times 8 =$ _____   **f)** $8 \times 9 =$ _____

5. Answer these questions.

    a) $36 \div 6 =$ _____   **b)** $45 \div 9 =$ _____   **c)** $49 \div 7 =$ _____

    d) $56 \div 7 =$ _____   **e)** $72 \div 8 =$ _____   **f)** $63 \div 9 =$ _____

6. Multiply each number by 4

    a) 30 → _____   **b) 40** → _____   **c) 60** → _____

    d) 300 → _____   **e) 500** → _____   **f) 900** → _____

7. Use partitioning to multiply these numbers.

    a) $27 \times 4 =$ _____   **b)** $54 \times 5 =$ _____   **c)** $49 \times 6 =$ _____

    d) $247 \times 6 =$ _____   **e)** $423 \times 7 =$ _____   **f)** $732 \times 8 =$ _____

Factors

 **Did you know...?** Factors are whole numbers that divide exactly into another number. To find the factors of **18** we:

- Look for pairs of numbers that multiply to make **18** $\boxed{1 \times 18}$ $\boxed{2 \times 9}$ $\boxed{3 \times 6}$

- Write the numbers in order **1, 2, 3, 6, 9, 18**. These are the factors of **18**

Finding factors

 1. On the petals write the factors of the number in the flower.

a)
12

b)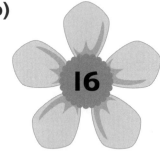
16

c)
24

d)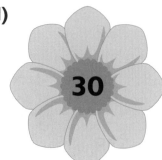
30

e)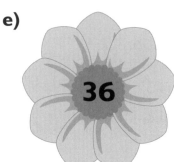
36

f)
42

Using factors

Using factors can make multiplying in our heads easier. Watch this:

25 × 18

6 and **3** are factors of **18**, so, we can break **18** into **6 × 3** and the question becomes:

25 × 6 × 3

25 × 6 = 150 and **150 × 3 = 450**, so **25 × 18 = 450**

 2. Use factors to help you answer these questions.

a) **25 × 8 =** _____   b) **15 × 6 =** _____   c) **25 × 12 =** _____

d) **30 × 14 =** _____   e) **30 × 16 =** _____   f) **40 × 12 =** _____

g) **40 × 15 =** _____   h) **35 × 12 =** _____   i) **45 × 16 =** _____

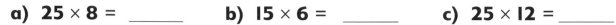

The grid method of multiplication

Grid multiplication

Grid multiplication uses the partitioning we looked at on page 16.

We split the numbers into hundreds, tens and units or even thousands, hundreds, tens and units and we multiply them separately. Then we add all the answers together.

7 × 6234   Always get an approximate answer first: **6000 × 7 = 42 000**

$$7 \times 6\ 2\ 3\ 4$$

$$6000 \quad 200 \quad 30 \quad 4$$

×	42 000	1400	210	28
7					= 43 638

Check the answer against your approximation.

I. Use grid multiplication to multiply these numbers.

a) 4 × 248

×	200	40	8
4				= _____

b) 5 × 387

×	300	80	7
5				= _____

c) 6 × 472

×			
				= _____

d) 7 × 539

×			
				= _____

e) 632 × 8

				= _____

f) 746 × 9

				= _____

g) 4 × 2634

				= _____

h) 5 × 3628

				= _____

i) 6 × 5729

				= _____

j) 7 × 6285

				= _____

Other methods of multiplication

Column multiplication

When you are confident about using grid multiplication you can shorten the method.

7 × 6234   Approximately **7 × 6000 = 42 000**

```
              6 2 3 4
          ×         7
7 × 6000 →  4 2 0 0 0
7 × 200  →    1 4 0 0
7 × 30   →      2 1 0
7 × 4    →        2 8
            4 3 6 3 8
```
Check the answer against your approximation.

1. Use this column method to multiply these numbers.

    a) **5 × 463 = _____**   b) **4 × 572 = _____**   c) **486 × 6 = _____**

    d) **2356 × 5 = _____**   e) **6219 × 7 = _____**   f) **8 × 7472 = _____**

Short multiplication

When you are confident about using column multiplication you can shorten the method. Follow the boxes if you are not sure.

7 × 6234   Approximately **7 × 6000 = 42 000**

```
        6 2 3 4
    ×         7
    4 3 6 3 8
      1 2 2
```
Check the answer against your approximation.

| (7 × 6) + 1 = 43 Write 43 | (7 × 2) + 2 = 16 Write 6 and carry 1 thousand into the thousands column. | (7 × 3) + 2 = 23 Write 3 in the tens column and carry 2 hundreds into the hundreds column. | (7 × 4) = 28 Write 8 and carry 2 tens into the tens column. |

2. Use this shorter method to multiply these numbers.

    a) **357 × 4 = _____**   b) **618 × 5 = _____**   c) **6 × 726 = _____**

    d) **3086 × 4 = _____**   e) **5429 × 7 = _____**   f) **8 × 6374 = _____**

Multiplying by tens and units

Multiplying larger numbers

Sometimes we have to multiply by **2**-digit numbers. We can do it using the grid method like this:

24 × 682   Always get an approximate answer first: **20 × 700 = 14 000**

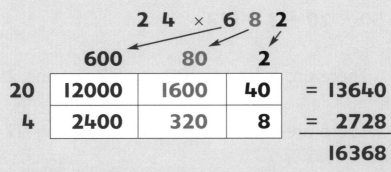

	600	80	2	
20	12000	1600	40	= 13640
4	2400	320	8	= 2728
				16368

Check the answer against your approximation.

1. Use this method to multiply these numbers.

a) 17 × 341 = _____   b) 32 × 453 = _____   c) 45 × 516 = _____

d) 362 × 57 = _____   e) 473 × 38 = _____   f) 603 × 54 = _____

Here is another way:

527 × 36   Approximately **500 × 40 = 20 000**

```
            527
        ×    36
30 × 527 →  I 5 8 I 0
6 × 527 →     3 I 6 2
            I 8 9 7 2
```

Because the answer to **30 × 527** will be **10** times larger than **3 × 527**, put a **0** to make the answer **10** times larger and then multiply **527** by **3**.

Multiply **527** by **6**.

Check the answer against your approximation.

2. Use this method to multiply these numbers.

a) 327 × 24 = _____   b) 462 × 43 = _____   c) 538 × 56 = _____

d) 639 × 58 = _____   e) 8027 × 48 = _____   f) 8735 × 97 = _____

Written division

Written division

You'll need to be able to divide on paper. Here is one way, using easy number facts.

692 ÷ 4   *Approximately* **700 ÷ 4 = 175**

$$100 + 50 + 20 + 3 = 173$$

$$4\overline{)692}$$

4 × 100   **−400** →   There are **4** lots of **100** in **692**, leaving **292**
              292 left

4 × 50   **−200** →   There are **4** lots of **50** in **292**, leaving **92**
              92 left

4 × 20   **−80** →   There are **4** lots of **20** in **92**, leaving **12**
              12 left

4 × 3   **−12** →   There are **4** lots of **3** in **12**, leaving **0**
              0 left

1. Try these questions on scrap paper using the method above.

a) $5\overline{)135}$ b) $6\overline{)138}$ c) $7\overline{)147}$

d) $6\overline{)378}$ e) $5\overline{)235}$ f) $8\overline{)456}$

Shorter methods of division

Here are some other ways of dividing:

$$150 + 23 = 173$$
$$4\overline{)692}$$

4 × 150   **−600**
              92
4 × 23   **−92**
              0

> This is a shorter version of the method above, where we start with **4 × 150** rather than **4 × 100**. We can use whatever facts we know.

$$\begin{array}{r} 1\ 7\ 3 \\ 4\overline{)6\,^2 9\,^1 2} \end{array}$$

> This is often called short division. **4** into **6 = 1 r 2**. Write **1** above. Carry **2** to make **29**. **4** into **29 = 7 r 1**. Write **7** above. Carry **1** to make **12**. **4** into **12 = 3**. Write **3** above.

2. Try these questions, using one of the methods above.

a) $5\overline{)185}$ b) $6\overline{)186}$ c) $7\overline{)168}$

d) **438 ÷ 6 = _____**   e) **656 ÷ 8 = _____**   f) **783 ÷ 9 = _____**

Multiplying decimals

Did you know...? We can multiply decimals in the same way we multiply whole numbers. Always approximate first because then we don't have to worry about the decimal points. Now multiply as if they were whole numbers.

7·84 × 6 *Approximate:* **8 × 6 = 48**

$$
\begin{array}{r}
784 \\
\times \quad 6 \\
\hline
\end{array}
$$

700 × 6 →	4200
80 × 6 →	480
4 × 6 →	24

$$\overline{47\cdot04}$$

2·34 × 2·6 *Approximate:* **2 × 3 = 6**

$$
\begin{array}{r}
234 \\
\times \quad 26 \\
\hline
\end{array}
$$

234 × 20 →	4680
234 × 6 →	1404

$$\overline{6\cdot084}$$

The answer must be **47·04** rather than **4·704** or **470·4** because our approximation was **48**

The answer must be **6·084** rather than **60·84** or **608·4** because our approximation was **6**

1. Multiply these decimal numbers.

a) **5·6 × 7** = _____

b) **7·8 × 5** = _____

c) **8·3 × 6** = _____

d) **6·45 × 4** = _____

e) **6·04 × 7** = _____

f) **2·39 × 8** = _____

2. Now try these.

a) **3·25 × 4·8** = _____

b) **4·86 × 3·2** = _____

c) **6·28 × 5·7** = _____

d) **7·89 × 4·9** = _____

e) **8·93 × 6·2** = _____

f) **9·04 × 7·8** = _____

Dividing decimals

Did you know... We can divide decimals in the same way we divide whole numbers. Always approximate first because then we don't have to worry about the decimal points. Now divide as if they were whole numbers.

19·5 ÷ 5   *Approximate:* **19·5** is about **20** and **20 ÷ 5 = 4**.

$$\begin{array}{r} 3\ \ 9 \rightarrow 3\cdot9 \\ 5\overline{)1\ 9\ ^45} \end{array}$$

5 into **19** = **3** r **4**. Write **3** above. Carry **4** to make **45**. **5** into **45** = **9**. Write **9** above. Look at the approximation to decide where to put the decimal point.

The answer must be **3·9** rather than **39** or **0·39** because our approximation was **4**.

1. Divide these numbers and shade in your answers in the grid below.

a) $5\overline{)14\cdot5}$

b) $6\overline{)15\cdot6}$

c) $7\overline{)21\cdot7}$

d) $6\overline{)8\cdot76}$

e) $5\overline{)9\cdot85}$

f) $8\overline{)8\cdot64}$

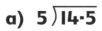

g) **65·1 ÷ 7 = _____**

h) **5·16 ÷ 6 = _____**

i) **7·56 ÷ 9 = ____**

j) **41·88 ÷ 6 = _____**

k) **10·88 ÷ 8 = _____**

l) **164·5 ÷ 7 = ____**

1·36	2·4	3·87	1·9	4·82	3·6
23·5	4·04	9·27	3·1	1·46	9·3
2·9	0·84	2·6	6·98	8·1	0·86
8·3	7·56	4·9	3·7	8·64	1·97
2·7	0·46	6·2	4·86	3·9	1·08

Word problems

Solving word problems

When faced with a problem, follow these steps:

- Read the problem carefully.
- Look for any useful words in the question.
- Write down any important numbers in the question.
- Decide how to work it out.
- Get an approximate answer, work it out, then check.

*Petrol costs **78·5p** per litre. How much will it cost me to put **18** litres in my car?*

- Petrol is **78·5p** for each litre.
- Multiply **78·5p** by **18** to find the cost of **18** litres.
- Work it out: **78·5 × 18 = £14.13**
- Check with the approximate answer.

*Remember always to approximate: **80p × 20 = 1600p** or **£16***

1. Petrol costs **82·4p** per litre.
How much will it cost to put **15** litres in my car?

_____

2. How much will each person earn in a **year**?

   a) Annette Curtain earns **£2056** per **month**.

_____

   b) Theresa Green earns **£438.50** per **week**.
   (Use **1** year equal to **52** weeks)

_____

3. Hawsker school has **480** pupils in **15** classes.
What is the average number of pupils in each class?

_____

Final Test

1. Use these facts to help you to answer the questions below.

| 42 ÷ 7 = 6 | 9 × 8 = 72 | 54 ÷ 6 = 9 |

a) 72 ÷ 8 = _____   b) 9 × 6 = _____   c) 6 × 7 = _____

2. Answer these questions.

a) 8 × 7 = ____   b) 7 × 9 = ____   c) 5 × 8 = ____   d) 7 × 7 = ____

e) 8 × 6 = ____   f) 9 × 5 = ____   g) 4 × 7 = ____   h) 9 × 3 = ____

3. To answer these questions, **double** the first number and **halve** the other.

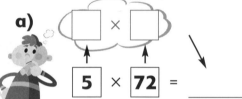
a) 5 × 72 = _____

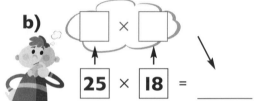
b) 25 × 18 = _____

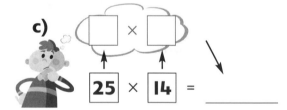
c) 25 × 14 = _____

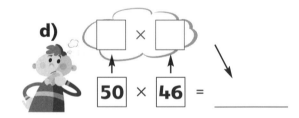
d) 50 × 46 = _____

4. Multiply these numbers by 10

a) 29   → _____   b) 608 → _____   c) 9127 → _____

5. Multiply these numbers by 100

a) 24   → _____   b) 536 → _____   c) 8267 → _____

6. Divide these numbers by 10

    a) 730 → _____

    b) 1690 → _____

    c) 3000 → _____

7. Divide these numbers by 100

    a) 6200 → _____

    b) 7300 → _____

    c) 86 000 → _____

8. Answer these questions, giving answers with remainders.

    a) $39 \div 4 =$ _____

    b) $68 \div 7 =$ _____

    c) $57 \div 8 =$ _____

9. Write the factors of these numbers.

    a) 32 → _____

    b) 72 → _____

10. Use factors to help you answer these questions.

    a) $25 \times 12 =$ _____

    b) $45 \times 14 =$ _____

11. Use any method you choose to multiply these numbers.

    a) $5 \times 572 =$ _____

    b) $6826 \times 9 =$ _____

12. Use any method you choose to multiply these numbers.

    a)   729
       ×   58

    b)   3804
       ×   75

13. Use any method you choose to divide these numbers.

    a) $6\overline{)564}$ **b)** $8\overline{)768}$

14. Multiply these decimal numbers.

    a) $3\cdot95 \times 8 =$ _____   **b)** $4\cdot37 \times 5\cdot2 =$ _____

15. Divide these decimals.

    a) $34\cdot8 \div 6 =$ _____   **b)** $6\cdot84 \div 9 =$ _____

16. Solve this problem.

    784 sweets are divided equally into **14** bags.
    How many sweets are there in **5** bags?   _____